My Socks

by
Julie Igel, CCH

Illustrated by Pearly L.

My Socks
by Julie Igel, CCH
Illustrated by Pearly Lim

Published by
Three Hedgehog Press
Oceanside, California

Three Hedgehog Press

Library of Congress Control Number: 2020945490
ISBN: 978-1-7355895-0-3

This book is dedicated to
my three amazing girls, Nichole, Gabby and Nadia,
who inspired this book and continue to inspire me on a daily basis—I love you!

To my husband Helmut,
the best papa ever and to a job well done—I love you too!!

And to all the parents out there, working hard to support their
sensitive children—I applaud you!

I hope this book brings a smile to your day!

I don't like my socks.
I don't like them at all.

When my mom puts them on me,
I run down the hall.

I can't stand
the feel of my toes in between.

There's something about them that makes me go crazy.
I'm not sure why— it's all sort of hazy.

My mom's tried and tried to get me to wear them— different colors and styles, some even have gems.

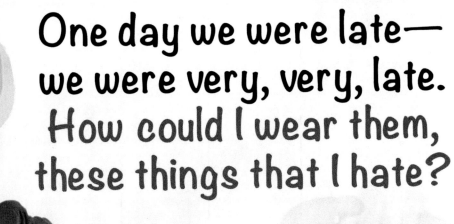

One day we were late—
we were very, very, late.
How could I wear them,
these things that I hate?

She chased me, she did.
Chased me for an hour.

When she finally caught me,
she looked pretty sour.

She was about to give up.
I thought I had won.
Can you keep a secret?
It was really quite fun!

But then something changed.
There would be no defeat.
She turned my sock inside out
and grabbed one of my feet.

On went the sock, so fast and so quick.
It was like some sort of magical trick.

We were both very quiet—
not a sound in the air.
Then before we
both knew it,
I was wearing the pair.

Something changed with my socks
when their insides were out.
They didn't bother me this way.
There was no need to pout!

My mom dried my tears
and gave me a high five.

We put on our smiles and headed outside!

Not everything is perfect
since that crazy day,
but I will wear my
socks now,
I am happy to say!

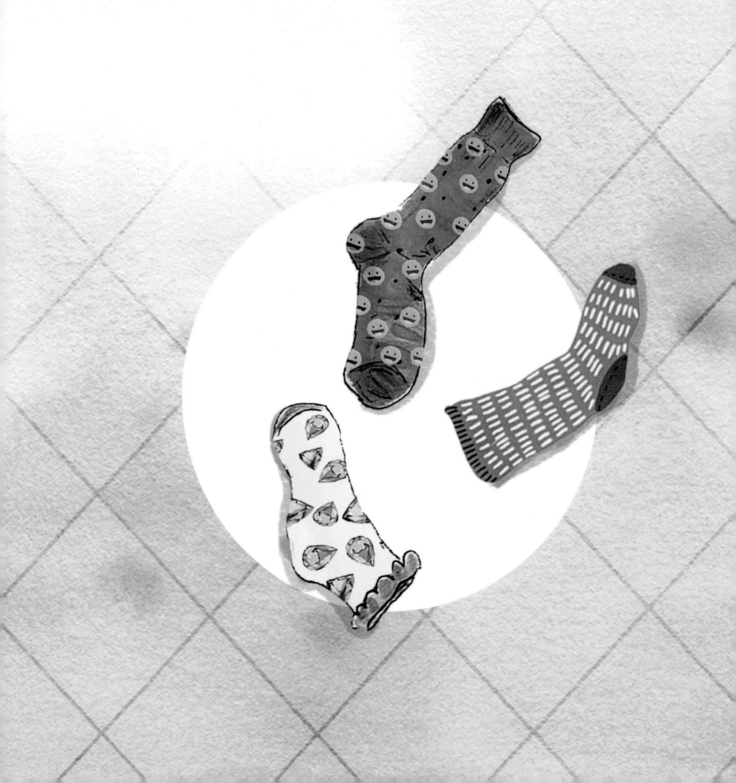

About the Author

Julie lives in San Diego, California, with her husband Helmut, and their two kitties. She is a Certified Classical Homeopath and has a private practice with clients all over the world. She created this book in honor of her three daughters, one of whom had sensitivities to all textiles, especially her socks! She hopes to support and encourage parents with similar children, share some laughter, and bring a smile to the challenge of parenting in this day and age.

Visit her website at
www.homeopathicSOULutions.com
or write to her
Julie@homeopathicsoulutions.com

About the Illustrator - With background in architecture and experience as an illustrator, interior and graphic designer, Pearly is passionate about all things design. She especially loves illustrating for children's book and working closely with authors to help bring their stories to life!

Made in the USA
Middletown, DE
25 March 2021

36239105R00015